"*Do I not, in speaking as I sense I must, exploit, for my own purpose, the uncanny beauty another man has made? They're spangled feathers—the lives, the achievements, the properties of others. Who among us does not have a nest to keep stewarded with all the glitter gatherable in reach? Let me tell you something: if the act of the profiteer is what we are talking about, then living better, for my part, couldn't be any better than my having lived long enough for me to enrich myself by dint of realizing the least proximity to the insuperably forged sentences of Jason Schwartz. As for the author, this mandarin heretofore hidden among us, there is positively nothing I can usefully say to you for him or of him or to him. He is complete, as genius agonizingly is. Can there be a more ghastly occupation? It is no guess that it had to have been terrible for Schwartz to have contained* John the Posthumous *and its equally uncontainable antecedent, the 1998 collection of sinuosities brought out as* A German Picturesque. *How reckless of Jason Schwartz for him to have recommended himself for the test of turning a totalized form of attention over to such a quality of suffering. Yes, the folly of it, declares your opportunistic intercessor. Oh, but how lucky the forerunner is!—how thrillingly, how terrifically, how unimprovably lucky.*"

—GORDON LISH

A GERMAN PICTURESQUE

"Grandly intrepid . . . In story after story, his cool language scrutinizes the world; behind this smooth prose seethe the violence and confusion of many lives, many acts . . . Unlike much so-called experimental fiction, Schwartz's work contains genuine passion and invention." —NEW YORK TIMES

"A careful construct of repeated words, phrases and description lends the book a steady, subtle pulse which belies a guiding inner logic that is entirely its own . . . Those whose idea of a good-time read is a literary Rubik's Cube have a colorful new toy on their hands." —DETROIT FREE PRESS

"An extraordinary, associative, allusive artist whose stories in scope, innuendo, subtlety are like reading T.S. Eliot in prose . . . Schwartz's pieces can keep a reader mystified in almost every way who, why, what, where but never in the perfect logic of sentences moving forward one after another: what comes next, comes next, most often brilliantly and sometimes breathtakingly . . . His vast but miniaturist genius is for seeing the enormous in the tiny, the significant in the silent, the horror-filled in the mute, the voicelessly poetic in almost everything."

—KIRKUS REVIEWS

JOHN the
POSTHUMOUS

ALSO BY JASON SCHWARTZ

A German Picturesque

JOHN the

POSTHUMOUS

JASON SCHWARTZ

OR Books

New York · London

© 2013 Jason Schwartz

Portions of this book first appeared in *American Letters & Commentary*,
The American Reader, *The Antioch Review*, *failbetter*, *Green Mountains Review*,
H_NGM_N, *New York Tyrant*, *Salt Hill*, *Unsaid*, and *Web Conjunctions*.

Published by OR Books, New York and London
Visit our website at www.orbooks.com

First printing 2013

Cataloging-in-Publication data is available from the Library of Congress.
A catalog record for this book is available from the British Library.

ISBN 978-1-939293-21-3 paperback
ISBN 978-1-939293-22-0 e-book

Typeset by Lapiz Digital, Chennai, India.
Printed by BookMobile in the United States and CPI Books Ltd in the United
Kingdom. The U.S. printed edition of this book comes on Forest Stewardship
Council-certified, 30% recycled paper. The printer, BookMobile, is 100%
wind-powered.

SUSAN POLLARD
1943–1998

CONTENTS

HORNBOOK

ONE

The maiden name—and then a list of the sisters.

Eleanor, the youngest, is first. From afar—the distance between the fencepost and the road, say, or between you and the house—she appears to fall into a well. In fact, she vanishes in the bracken. Audrey is smallest. Fire irons and a brown wall, a skirt with a nailhead pattern. Drawn curtains are rather less charming than a drowning—as the mother has it. While the bedsheets, according to that old saying, are the knives of the bed. Blanche, the eldest, is last. They imagine her struggling along, arriving at the wrong house. Or returning to the staircase, now more amply rouged.

The mother sits upright, apart from the father.

Whose brother—Edward, or perhaps Edmond— suffers quite elaborately. His humiliations, then—at a Western elevation, or as a boy, or one day in the fall.

They part on a boulevard, at the far end, near a park. Or near a harbor the following summer. And so on, as it rains into the front room. Where his daughter—you might observe, from above, the route of her departure— sits without a suitor. Her name—Gertrude, in blue ink— fails to account for the portrait of horses, the lampshade in the fireplace, the hour.

The grandmother, on the father's side, weeps in the greenery.

Her sister—Esther—lives on a finer street, east of here, near the river. She addresses herself to the brass doorstop—it is a rat in the purse, it turns out, and not a mouse—and then to her husband's ruined shoes. The husband—William, in cursive—is bedridden, or seems unwell, ill, if somewhat better now, curiously so, espe- cially in the evening. On the huntboard is a hand of pork, garnished with black olives—though he prefers green. His plate resembles a gray face, the knife covering the eyes.

The grandfather, on the father's side, points the blade this way.

His brother—the name is gone—returns at nine o'clock. Ten o'clock, as they imagine it—a train station and a lawn, a mishap on a bridge. Or a burnt hat-rack and a metal hook, his wife attired in a gown of some kind. The wife—Anne, or perhaps Anna—stands rather as your sister does, facing the drapery. Her possessions, then—on the windowsill, on the dressing table, in the bureau drawer. The bedpost, from a more sensible angle, might obscure a portion of the wardrobe, and divide the room in two.

TWO

I.

Corinthians begins with the salutation, and not, as I had thought, a description of locusts on a hilltop. Or even beetles in a forest, a woods, a copse—on pine trees, for instance, as behind our house. Chapter two cites "decline"—"I came before you in weakness, trembling"—though this offers little about a burning town. I imagine axles and a wagon wheel, somehow, and then an animal—its shriek, I should think, rather like the sound a child makes, crying out at night. Chapter three cites "fire"—in Romans, by contrast, a "wooden throat" follows a "page of flesh," or vice versa—beside "the tower" and "the house" and "the road." Silver, in a later passage, is placed at a wall or at a gate, despite the color of the jackals. Chapter four cites "rags," which, displayed thus, may remind you of certain birds, such as those lost at the falls. They were blinded, were they not? Or perhaps they died of fright. It was smoke or fog, according to that story—a great gray arrangement. The plumage was blue, yes, but I am partial to the rabbits in the bracken. Chapter five cites "Satan," even if, on occasion, the body is a boy's. The organs and the bones, anyway—though these are soon replaced with hay and straw. The latter is black—I hate to admit how this still gives my heart a start—and the garment white. Chapter six cites "thieves" and "adulterers"—rather than, as in Timothy, a "list of widows." The terms differ somewhat in the Egyptian conception, where demons accompany each affliction. Here, the canopy signifies—in one of the less extravagant descriptions—a crown. When the canopy depicts figures of the victim, or victims, the cords are red to indicate places of contagion. The sackcloth vanishes, I gather, from the other houses, north along the road.

Chapter seven contains the phrase in question.

In the Authorized Version (1611), the Common Version (1833), the English Revised Version (1881–1885), and the American Standard Version (1901), as well as

Wesley's New Testament (1755), Young's Literal (1862), and the Darby (1890): "It is better to marry than to burn."

Satan appears to the left of every phrase. So goes one old notion. Or, in some texts, to the left of every letter. On occasion, Satan appears to the right of—or, more rarely, behind—the number nine. And then he carries away the son's bones.

Various medieval diseases were named for the Devil—but then, so were doorframes of an especially peculiar design. When dead men appear as scorched walls, rather than within them—this was once thought evidence of the Devil. The Devil was once thought a bird in the blood. The variations, from section to section, would depend upon the configuration of limbs.

In several accounts, the Devil appears as a mute at a funeral.

The Wycliffe (1388)—"It is better to be wedded than to be burned"—is the translation by John Wycliffe, or Wiclif, whose corpse, according to one history, was exhumed, painted black, dismembered, and then presented in a wooden cage. Or, according to another history, exhumed, beheaded, and then burned in a churchyard, the ashes thrown into a river.

The Devil's animal, in the storybooks, is found at the father's house, sometimes composed of white rope. Brown cats, rather than black, are thrown at prisoners en route to the tower. The remains are green, or seem so—while a table hobbles in the next town.

Satan places the tablecloth, as they used to say. And then he slices through the parson's eye. The alderman's walk is set aside for the more prominent guests. A rabbit is brought out on its haunches, broiled, the ears having been removed at the roots.

A certain dog—often a dying one—is thought to recall a blue noose or a torn quilt at the foot of the bed.

The Douay-Rheims (1582)—"It is better to marry than to be burned"—was begun in Douay, or Douai, and completed in Rheims, or Reims. The translation—by Gregory Martin, a consumptive—was revised by, among others, Thomas Worthington and William Allen. The former, incidentally, married the latter's niece.

The Weymouth (1903)—"For marriage is better than the fever of passion"—is the translation by Richard Francis Weymouth, who died outside Essex in 1902.

Timothy sometimes appears as a sword or a dagger.

Paul sometimes appears as a dog with horns.

It was once customary to list all the names, the names of the saints and their afflictions, and the family names, and then the names of the places, in order, one end to the other—after the fashion of objects arranged on a gray table, or gray objects arranged in the countryside.

II.

In Leviticus, the adulterer and the adulteress are "put to death." Or, more precisely, they "must be" or "surely shall be"—depending upon the version of the text. The man who "lieth with his father's wife," furthermore, "hath uncovered his father's nakedness." Or, translated another way, "shame"—even if we prefer the simpler notion of folds or creases in a coat. They vanish, alas—or die, as the ancients might have phrased it—while you set the blanket aside. Numbers presents the wife, defiled or otherwise, and the jealous husband. The act is "secret," "without witness," "hidden from his eyes." The ordeal, in turn, calls for a burnt offering and bitter water, the recitation of an oath. In Deuteronomy, the father sets out the daughter's bedsheet. "Blood," however, has been omitted. Perhaps you imagine a circle, instead— a small circle—and then something worse. If a girl is betrothed, but lies with another man, and if she "cries not"—then "ye shall stone them," the girl and the man, at the city gate. Or at the town gate, if the girl is found in a town, as in a later version of the text. Hosea presents the marriage as unhappy—"I shall close the road with thorns"; "I shall ravage the vines." Garments— "the wool and the flax"—are found in a woods, we may suppose, rather than animals, blind and dying.

I am troubled by Susanna, as this was my mother's name. In my childhood Bible, I now recall, I scratched out the name in three places.

Matthew refers to a "lustful eye." This—or, more precisely, "your right eye"—should be "torn out," "cut out," "excised." In Peter—if we may break, for the moment, from the proper sequence—"they commit adultery with their eyes." Or, translated another way, their eyes are "full of adultery" and "cannot cease from sin." In John, the woman is brought to the temple in the morning. She stands "in the middle" or "in their midst," true, or "before them all"—but her attire is never described. The act is "the very act"—even later on, when you imagine the houses as faces, for instance, or as coffins. In Romans—as in Mark and Luke, most notably— "adultery" occurs first. Now fold back the bedsheet, this way, and you have a handsome old scene. The blanket, however, gathered at the throat—this is best thought a separate matter. Galatians refers to "works of the flesh." The phrase neglects the curtain, rent and burnt—as well as the hornets sewn into the daughter's gown. In Revelation, "I cast the adulteress onto a bed." Or—more elaborately—a "sickbed" or a "bed of suffering." The men "weep and mourn," watching the body burn.

III.

Corinthians concludes in far happier fashion, without further discussion of rupture, partition, divorce.

There is, nevertheless, a list of cities and towns, towns and cities—afire, as I recall, in five lines. I need not mention the trees—or, for that matter, the flowerpots outside our house, along the path, near the back door, which was painted gray one year and red another. Romans cites the Psalms—"Their throats are open tombs"; "They are strangers"—but this has little to do with sticks or branches, with embers or cinders, or with wives hiding in an arbor. A forest, by contrast, the description of a forest, as discovered in a handbook, a miscellany, an annual—this implies a romance of some kind, does it not? Galatians cites "the custody of law," though the words in the dirt— if this is any of our concern—may refer to murder. Or to thievery, more likely, with ash in place of hair and—on the occasion of a Jewish union—a pile of reeds. The garments darken in certain places, at least as I understand it—the throat, or the wrists and the throat, the seams appearing to bleed. Ephesians cites "children," which may explain a blot in the margin, say, if not the formation of horses on a shoreline. The birds at the falls, for their part—these were waterfowl of an ordinary variety, the sadder examples crippled or maimed. It was a lavish drowning, according to that story—a gentleman, or some other lonely figure, early in the morning, a thicket and a hilltop in the distance. Philippians cites "mutilation" and, elsewhere, "the book of life"—from which, in Exodus and the Psalms, the names of the dead are stricken, taken away, or otherwise excised.

In Deuteronomy and Isaiah: the husband writes the wife a "letter of divorce." Or a "certificate of divorce," a "bill of divorce," a "statement of divorce"—and then he sends her "from his home." In Jeremiah: the Lord writes Israel a "divorce notice"—with which, He says, "I put her away."

The mourner's concordance, so-called, lists the Devil first. This is for the letter A. But also second, for the letter B. And so on. Satan is often shown without a right hand—or with the letter X in its stead. The Devil is often shown without ears or a mouth.

The Devil was said to collect slights in a jar, quaint as that now sounds. His emblem is the split crow—a bird in two parts—on a field of red. In folklore, he sometimes assumes the face of a sad man. Satan waits inside a certain word—or with a family on a staircase.

The Devil, in the old pattern books, is a segment of black thread, one stitch below the throat.

In Esther: the king divorces the queen. In Ezra: one hundred husbands—among them, Elijah, Ishmael, Nethanel, Judah, Eliezer, Zechariah, Sheal, Adna, Simeon, Benjamin, Malluch, Amram, Nathan, Shallum, and Joseph—divorce their wives. Priests in the line of Joshua, furthermore, offer a ram in sacrifice.

Wolves and jackals, in the storybooks, are funeral animals. The sparrows are often drawn without claws. On Sundays—when the horses fall in the morning, or when the hunt is a fire hunt—the descriptions are less than generous.

The Devil arrives in due course, hidden behind the children.

Sexton beetles bury carrion—birds and rodents, for the most part. One superstition concerns the deacon's cat, which drowns in the rain. Another concerns the decapitation of oxen. Various other animals—such as those slaughtered on the town green—are named for Satan.

In our family Bible: the flyleaf is inscribed in blue ink, in a narrow hand. From husband to wife—followed by a month, a slash, a year. There is a curious break in the number eight. And a mark of sorts, a smudge—a tiny form in the corner of the page.

Matthew addresses the husbands and sons, now at some great distance from the river, from the plain, from the town.

Paul is all alone.

It was once customary to remove—with a table knife or a razor blade—the pages displaying the names of the wives. And for the forsaken—or the bereaved—to spell out the beloved's name on a white bedsheet, set the bedsheet afire, and then swallow the ashes.

THREE

The churches in Eaton, as in Lawton and Harrow, not to mention Putnam, Dunnock, Whitebriar, and Townsend—these, I believe, were destroyed during the war. In Newbury—where a child had died rather famously, a boy, the son of a minister or a deacon, the blackcoat, as they had it, drowned, his feet cut off for the coffin, which was then lost—the spire was a broach spire. In Bethlehem, the tower once housed four mourners—or five, were you to include the suicide—the chains arranged in a so-called hatchet pattern. (According to one old notion, red steeples are neither God's arms nor falling bodies—but, in fact, spikes in a crown.) The Durham remains were buried with the beds, just west of the road. The markers, for their part, stood twenty or thirty paces from the churchyard. And the sound of the wind—this was quite another matter, especially in Colonial towns. (Speyer is a German cathedral town—city, actually— on the Rhine.) The Thornton daughters suffered on a rooftop, and then a balcony, and then a knoll. The Bratton marriage documents indicate a church wedding in late May—but exhibit, in place of names, drawings of corpses. (According to another old notion, black steeples are coffins or a cuckold's horns.) The churches in Eaton were destroyed by cannon fire, I imagine— the bells having been removed to Mill Hall and Pike Fork, or to Woodbine and Barlow. In Marion—where a beadle, dressed in funeral weeds, had been stabbed through the hands, the staircase at the back of the chapel, or in a tower, his body carried out in the morning—the spire was a needle spire. In Bedminster, the tower once housed two prisoners—the first thrown to his doom, as they had it, and the second drawn and quartered, the remains sent north to the wrong town.

FOUR

The word *cuckold* also refers to certain insects. Take the cuckold fly—which is actually a beetle, and which feigns death quite gracefully. The claws are dark—red, to be exact, or perhaps black—and the body oddly marked. The brown-headed cowbird, incidentally, found in the New World, often in barn fires, is akin, given its most notable particulars, to the Old World cuckoo. *Cucking,* however, as in *cucking stool*—set at the culprit's door or lost at the bottom of a pond—derives from a different root entirely, I was surprised to find, implying, among other things, the outlines of clouds, a house pulled down, and four forms in mourning.

A gentleman carries his manners into every room, does he not?

The horns are white, at least in Colonial renderings, the preferred versions of these, such as the portraits displayed at a pillory or at a gallows, or the drawings nailed to a soldier's hands. The branding iron is of little interest here, whatever the letter—the cheek more likely than the neck, under most circumstances, and the neck more likely than the chest. The phrases, explained by location—Alton, Batten, Caul, and so on—date from the sixteenth century, perhaps a bit earlier, and—if I have this correctly—concern the design of bedposts and the placement of stakes. Or, in some commentaries, a blind horse in a barnyard—save for those editions in which the horse is a dog and the barnyard a forest. Either way, *horn* is akin to *hart*, as in *stag*—this offers the antlers, if nothing else—and accounts, of course, for *hornet*.

There are drawings of the shoreline.

She creased the first sheet, as you can see—once, and then again, lengthwise, the corner torn away. And now the inlet strangles a cat? Probably not. But remove the locust trees and you have a pleasant memory.

Wrecks are less common downriver, or upstream, or in the creek in the next town.

My, my—the rowboats and the hillside.

Writ of ravishment suggests an error of sorts, given the nature of the occasion, while *simple adultery*, in

American case law, will often accompany—among other ceremonial terms for the husband—*man of blood* and, in turn, *ghost at the feast*. The evidence usually includes several cheerful garments—here is the fearnaught, for instance, hanging in the attic—in addition to the children's things. Consider Burrows versus Burrows, 1878, Pennsylvania—despite the drawn curtains. Or Trumbull versus Trumbull, 1881, Connecticut—most notable for an accident on a balcony. Or Stark versus Cartwright, 1897, Maryland—in which a valise is stolen, and then mislaid, and later found in a lake. The table-setting that evening, left to right, right to left—which is to say, the view of the suitor from the road—is small consolation, I know.

The garden calendar calls for jackroot, a plant of the beggar-ticks variety.

Bestiaries, especially Spanish versions—the miniatures in particular, circa fifteenth century—depict the horns quite modestly. Spikes give way to branches, though these may be mistaken for antlers or hands, after the fashion of other Christian depictions—in which, furthermore, a crucifix appears between the eyes. The pointed cross, also called the cross fitchee,

23

takes a different form for demons and thieves, and, in Dutch versions, burns to the ground. English versions, finally, provide curious explanations of the glaive, the dudgeon, the halberd, the broadax—the wives die even as we speak—and then an apology for the paltry lawn.

August arrives in due course, the color of a statue or a hatchet.

But this does overstate it somewhat.

A window, three doors, the roofline. They sat on the balcony in the morning. And now the water is apparent between the trees? From above, these suggest horseflesh.

Blight, it turns out, is less likely than rot—as you will see in the fall.

English canon law allows for mention of a hedgerow, or, in lieu of this, a narrative about a black house, beginning with two formal locutions in the corner room. The first concerns a murder—*machination* is considered the more appropriate term, at least in these dioceses—while the second is a confession, neatly abridged. Here we have the alcove bed, for instance, from 1793, made up in gray. The trestle bed, from 1810, resembles—if I may beg your indulgence—a trembling man. The canopy bed, from 1819, from 1822, from 1827, hides ten items. A treatise on drapery follows, regarding, in part, a brace of grouse and a saddle of mutton, or—depending upon the sadness of the family—green chains and a windowsill.

The landscape plan mistakes the location of the garden wall.

Hoddypoll, which also means *fool,* I believe, derives from *dod*—as in *snail* and *small hill*—and from *koll*—which is Norwegian for *head* or *crown,* and is the root of *kill.* We may find *doddard,* then, in the beheading of a gentleman in the fifteenth century—but *dodder,* by the sixteenth century, for a kind of chokeweed or for a body shaking in pain. *Kellen* implies neither a corruption of *poison* nor an argument for *catgut,* despite the scarechild—a torn rag with brass eyes—in the basket. *Buck's-head,* a later variation, presents happier facts—one's wife repairs to the country, surveys the scenery, returns home in the evening—but disappears by the nineteenth century.

The drawings of the shoreline are rather inexact.
Five—I have five.

She cut out a little square, and then another—and in this way made the faces. You would prefer a brick walk and a privet? Certain of the words resemble ants in distress.

The lake is named for the town, or for an animal, and is shaped like an ax-blade.

Adulterium, as defined by the Julian Statute, circa 13 B.C., offers fewer charms, given the particulars of winter, not to mention various old-fashioned sentiments concerning execution. Mutilation, for its part, is more common—the adulterous wife, or *adultera*, to use the legal term, surrenders her ears or nose, and, on occasion, her fingers—with divorce following in short order. Some transcriptions neglect the stranger, or *adulter*, in favor of graves—a simple matter of manners, this, notwithstanding the disquisition upon the marriage bed. Others relate ordinary household details—dismantling the chairs, and visiting the windows, and departing the courtyard.

A gentleman, remember, always averts his eyes.

Cuckold's Point, near Brockwell, in London, is most notable for its gallows—the red sticks recall horns—and for the drowning of dogs. A cuckold's neck requires a spar or beam, as I understand it, unlike the Matthew Walker found on the fainting couch, or the nail hitch found among the movables in the front room. The hangman's knot, with seven coils, or even eight, as per custom—the shade of brown is often a subject of debate—fails to explain the odd formation of lampposts on the avenue. Colonial towns preferred a woolen hood, manacles and chains, and—regarding the father—the scaffold painted black.

FIVE

The foregoing ignores—or mistakes—several details. Cuckold's Point, according to the map I have in hand, is closer to Evelyn than to Deptford. And Brockwell, strictly speaking, does not exist—in London, anyway. Furthermore, the horned figure—now gone—was not a gallows, in fact, but a simple post. It had been exhibited at a fair—the Horn Fair—in celebration of a king's cuckolding. Which king? King Richard or King Edward. (John the Posthumous—usually rendered in red—was a French king, alive for five days.) The fair would occur every October, on Saint Luke's Day. The houses, like the tower, were south of the river, and were torn down in due course. A gibbet—absent, however, any configuration of slats or bars or sticks that might suggest horns—once stood ten or twenty paces from the road. Perhaps the murder had occurred on a doorstep. The cage, on this occasion, was made to recall the human form. (The remains of a certain William Fine, a Jew, were exhibited here for seven years and then removed to another gibbet, in Houndsditch.) Fragments of such contraptions—thought to cure various ailments—were sold at auction. Or stolen in town, as the case may be. The procession would pass through Lock Park and Blackton—the latter the site of a cattle market, a naval yard, an arsenal—and conclude in Charlton, for the sermon. The men wore horns. The carts, as I understand it, were dismantled at the end of the day—the wood stacked and then set afire.

SIX

The soldier—a redcoat, by all reports—chokes on a coin or a nail or, more likely, dead bees, three or four of them, shown here in a gray basin and on a white bedsheet. (Better a high bed, as the saying has it, than the sound of blood.) The sound of the blade—the implement is a short dagger rather than a mortuary sword—carries very well. Or so goes one description of the event, despite the burnt curtains, the slaughtered dog, the music in the attic. (A bruit, for its part, is a noise—a fault—in the heart.) The arms, in this formation—a martlet proper, at the battlement; shield, pommel, and hilt vert—are thought silent with regard to a falling body, for instance, or a sinking ship.

The crying wife, in folklore, is carried from a house— a burning house, in those unfortunate drawings—and then down a road and through a town—or across a field and through a forest—in a wooden bed. (The cannons seem charmless from this angle.) Thence south, perhaps, in a rainstorm, past the sorrow in the burrows, the jackchain and the shooting wall, and now, near a creek or a lake, the sounds of a drowning. A family stands in the grass—the boards red in the background, the steeples green. (Her heart went white, as the saying has it—or, more precisely, silent.) The nightdress is woolen, a plain design, open at the collar or fastened there with a clasp or a knot or just a common pin, the click of which may suggest an insect. (Hessian flies are Russian, in fact, and are sometimes confused with wasps.) Marks on a door, often a collection of scrapes or engravings, can indicate the loss of a daughter.

The orphan swallows a small bird, a finch or a sparrow, even a parakeet, wings clipped, eyes excised—at least as the narrative survives in the upland boroughs and in several of the Eastern towns. (Bloodbirds, so-called, are said to produce a rueful sound.) A bloody bone is thunder, in one version, and timber and chimney smoke, in another—or a pile of sticks near a river, just before the war. (The treetops seem to shriek.) A rag doll gives way to a stump doll—the face stained red, for the frightened child, or blue, for the dying child—which gives way, in turn, to a toy horse, described in a faltering voice. The rattlebox contains a hook and a blade, and is buried at the margin of the yard.

SEVEN

The *brown-headed cowbird*—as distinct from the *white-throated finch*, which attacks cattle—is entirely gray, in fact, in the female. These are apparent at your attic windows, three and three, at the end of the season. Several examples, wounded in the usual ways, can be found beside the house, in the flowerbed and in plants of the horsetail variety.

Weeds, properly speaking.

Pigeon's neck refers to a pinewood gunstock. *Pigeon's wing* refers to a shade of blue—but also to a knitting stitch and to a bloody wig.

Crow is an old parlor game, in which the family hides from the youngest son. *House sparrow* requires a child, a length of thread, and two birds.

Leave them there a moment.

The *fool hen* is brown, in the female, and spotted

white—with a black throat—in the male. These are drawn like ordinary barn-door fowl—the throat slit for the windpipe and crop, and then the vent for the heart, gizzard, and so on. It is correct to serve with cabbage and apples, or with pickled beets.

Your father does the carving.

Pigeon's bone refers to a manacle or a shackle, especially at a hanging. *Pigeon's blood* refers to a shade of red.

House sparrow is played in the country, on Sunday afternoons, at wakes and the like. *Crow* concludes in a dark room.

EIGHT

The ants: in parts.

The choke seeps blood and then withers in the cold. The heart recalls a needle, crooked at one end.

At night, as here, they can appear rather despairing.

I compare them with cornfields and with fathers in the dark, though wasps would surely posit a better resemblance.

Potters, for instance, are the correct color, among other things. White spears are without eyes.

Hook ants pass the fall in dooryards.

My advice: ox-gall, turpentine, and boiling water.

It is best to set the bait in a modest trap, slit dirt at either side. Some household objects, such as a hatbox or a milk tin, their tops properly gouged, will do just fine. Suffocation is often the easiest course later in the season.

Fire, for its part, prefers girls in a hayloft.

Never mind a lavish appraisal of the landscape, though, save for the remains of the stables.

Cattlehouses attract botflies, which resemble bees, generally speaking. Their maggots give sheep the staggers. Warble flies, lost, sometimes freeze on the green.

The winter passes handsomely.

And then: hornworms and betsys.

But cut leaves, as such, can also mean lash rot, a fever of sorts, with wounds somewhat graceless in formation, while the mottling seems more appropriate to a pox.

Thief ants occur inside decaying trees.

Shadows never help matters, dividing the bed lengthwise. The yard is dark by eight o'clock.

I do not expect guests anymore, no, but just look at all the cracks in the glass.

My apologies: for the black ink, for the meager portion of cloth.

It is sensible to use arsenic too, though mold will grow anyway. The parts are apparent at the bottom of the jar. The specimen should be placed on bright white paper, after the usual fashion, the block on end.

Light dictates the arrangement of pins.

A ridge replaces each appendage, in the male, the skin dull on the dorsal side.

The face displays a jaw and three sutures. The thorax follows from a notch, red in the terminal segment.

See the bees atop the cinders.

But spiders prefer flesh flies, which prefer pox hens, bleeding through the evening.

Tomorrow you will mistake them for postholes in a row.

The border plants, an afterthought, are caught by blight. The bruises ruin the view of the column and the vines.

To catch vermin of this sort, first turn back your cuffs, please, and remove your necktie, and then soak the roots in kerosene, cinching the rag with twine.

But now I have managed to trample the annuals again.

Certain courtesies also obtain in the case of stakes, beginning at said point in the northeast corner, and running thence west to the decline.

Solitary wasps occur in the rockery, one chain away.

Potters, for instance, hunt at the far end, stalks and all. The male seems to gasp.

When they surrender, examples of this family, the bodies shudder, barkweed strangling flowers in the background.

I neglect the pots and lose another month.

The trees follow rather solemnly from the fence, wounds painted red. The hedgerow narrows as it approaches the rats.

The deportment of the lawn accounts for my fall, northerly in performance, beginning at a distant point on the eastern side of the house, and concluding in the rain.

These beetles starve beneath the leaves.

Betsys trap weeps in better weather. Skins lie abed in the winter, the way one's mother sometimes does.

Bury carrion by the bracken, please, using a new spade and a tin bucket, your handkerchief set out like so, bees at the very edge of the image.

The hornets: in order.

Ours, for instance, are known to swarm about a sickroom. They die inside the lowboy.

In embroidered form, as here, the face displays a red stitch.

The veins take a different color, panel out. The thorns are ornamental.

Never mind that the blanket recalls an animal, from one angle, or that the flies collect in piles.

Other insects are even less congenial, given the habits of the household.

Such as: waiting at the window.

The scars on the doors are a better measure, however, like hatpins, and like the disposition of copper pots at five o'clock.

A calf's head, divided, accounts for the gnats. The heart decays on a polite white plate.

It is correct, I hope, to remove knives from left to right, and the glasses last. This one has cracked in my absence.

The hallway offers its own disappointments, beginning here, in poor light, and following discreetly to the gash in the far wall.

Deathwatch beetles will attack woodwork of this variety.

And then: the joists and cripples.

The ticking sound, once thought a final sign, is actually a fact of courtship.

I imagine the jaw as a broken line or as a simple triangle, the points in gray. A circle replaces the cranium proper.

Termites prefer timbers such as these. Fire sometimes traps rats in their galleries or behind an attic door.

Cellar stairs attract the smaller daughters, not to mention spiders and rot.

Or: toppled objects.

The gap in the banister is dreadfully evident, at any rate, despite the embarrassment of the pattern, hornets and all.

These examples are brown, with red banding and ordinary black claws. The veins are sickle-shaped.

The weal resembles a weal, I expect, though it weeps rather than bleeds.

Shadows appear at the furnace, given the hour, and given the matter of the housecoat and the ax.

The floor darkens accordingly.

NINE

The bed recurs as a figure in certain burnings—the torches fixed to boards, for skeletons, and the boiling oil in pots, in urns, in bowls.

But I am comporting myself poorly.

To begin again.

Camastro, a Spanish word, meant *wretched bed* in those days. As distinct from *camastro,* or *wicked bed*, given the facts of dialect. But then—the bodies lay east to west, did they not? And you can see how she clutched at her throat.

The Gothic style, in most tragic accounts, dispenses with mischief of this variety. Though it retains a collection of birds, for what that is worth—crows and so forth. Its posts, especially, may remind you of tombs of the period. Or of, more remotely, those relations, the very sad ones, who once came for the day.

The parable of the bed—I imagine the Bible contains no such item. What delicate phrases we must, therefore, do without. Tin knives and burnt blankets, a plague gate. Buried nightdresses, whether diseased or in pieces, find considerable favor in chronicles of a more Teutonic sort. While the parable of the gown ends, once again, without evidence of my wife.

My mother's will—it was innocent of various provisions. As distinct from common Colonial wills, for instance, whose clauses divide bed from body. So to say. Headboards, for the children, and linens, for the oven, and that canopy—which can only ruin your room, my dear. Some include codicils that explain the placement of mutes around the graves. And portraits of mourning scenes, the names—or a description of the illness, as the case may be—written out in place of the faces. I see, here, two girls who sit as my daughters do. And a fragment of glass that carries us entirely too far from our topic.

Jewish beds, in the New World, were often stuffed with cloth. Though black straw, of the type you might find in an effigy, was the custom in a number of towns. Older practices required ash. The skinner marked the carcass. Slaughter boys, so-called, crossed the boards and burned the offal. The family tore the cord. The marriage bed, in this brown house, was a prettier affair—the latch adorned with short spikes, on the husband's side, and short hooks, on the wife's. The hinge was neither gold nor silver, alas. Whereas the pock— this was copper. Sometimes the posts and slats were mistaken for bones. As distinct from skeletons, which sometimes travel to the attic in these marital narratives. Early embalming tables, it turns out, had been modeled upon early cradles. In Northern cities, during the war—the base and legs adorned with dagger-and-dart forms. True, the jars of arsenic were always kept apart from the tunic. Be gracious, please, and leave a place for the grave goods. Rings, for instance—which soldiers often wore pinned to their skin. There were other formalities for a family in a house.

If the morning is cold: begin with the scars at the bottom. Rot might follow the stains. For cubits, consider measuring endwise, pulling smartly at the hem. Subtract the width of one digit for every flaw. An insect might well be our culprit, after all. When facing south: the house appears to drown. Now the hour is happier but dim. For shaftments, measure the posts only, halving the rust at the bolt. Indicate the span with both hands, as though to signify fright or defeat. In the dark: the nail speaks ill of the glass. For inches, count seams by threes, board to board, quietly. Exclude the shadows at the near side. The wool will shift above you.

Camastro, or *wretched bed*, described a wooden contraption. Though the pikes were overtaken, in their way, by chains. The cell merits fuller treatment in this respect, despite the steel collar. And despite the harrow sticks, which, like the bodies, lay east to west. *Seize* was preferred, in those days, to *grasp* or *hold*. But now we think of our brother's hands, do we not? The cushions contained bees on these occasions, wasps on others. In plague cases, the hair turned first.

Wedding beds, in Pennsylvania, were stuffed with horsehair and pig bristle. Or, under the oddest of circumstances, girls' hair and poisoned soil. Bridal beds, in Maryland, used plain straw. Of the madder family—like Quaker-ladies or this bit of blue in the distance. Or like dying nightdress with a very low throat. Early weeds were evidently better than late ones, whose forms, anyway, sometimes recalled split tongues. Fur, for its part, was shorn according to rather primitive rules—peculiar knives, in the course of things—and piled with the skins. These burned especially well. Matrimonial beds, in New York, were cut open and emptied of feathers. Or they were wheeled to a gate and taken away in the rain.

The Colonial fourposter style—notice how poorly it conforms to the walls, to the crude themes of my room. One morning in a childhood home—with Mother and all, for what that is worth. The frame, painted gray, and the body, face down, and the bedsheet—whose seam is a shame, prominent as it is. Now fold the blanket like so. Find the scorch mark at the neck, as you always do. Watch the child show sorrow. Does one confess to the inheritance of bedclothes? *Bed,* in any case, once meant *flay*, as in a burr mattock or a beggar's cup, its handle a long nail. The hornbook—found north of the slaughter, or south of it—displays a drawing of boys. They stagger elaborately—or so it seems to me—outside a burning house. A diagram explains the demolition of a bed.

Beds of the dead, in Biblical custom, were buried, yes—usually at night, by the father. Though my father, perhaps like yours, died first. The garment is rent, in Jewish funeral law, which also requires that the eldest son fall to his knees. Well, if not this, quite, then certainly that the *shomer*, or watcher, exhibit the holes. The family cleaned the bones with lye. They scratched the ground. The reeds were brought to a wall. Morgue drawers, or stalls, were named and then dismantled. Rings were excised from the soldiers' skin—in the square, before the mourners. Mauled horses were sometimes found on the lawn. Is it true that little girls once had rooms like these? Let us try, next time, to save the nuns and lanterns on the staircase, and to describe the tombs with more aplomb. Oak coffins, in some traditions, were used in the event of contagion. The folded hands may remind you of knives—of the period or otherwise. Or of rats atop the bedsheets. Blankets, in many Colonial towns, were detailed with figures of husband and wife, the limbs spotted red or cut off—as the case may be—and the faces stuck with pins. Crying-houses, so-called, killed blind children in the night.

When fire arrives in those old towns: it is mistaken for flower carts or hospital wagons. And then the flames have their way with the drapery. An object ignites, it was thought, according to the form of its name. A rail—granted—before a rope, and paper—such as this—before a person. The way a body burns: this will embarrass us somewhat less. Brass makes little claim upon the seams. Batting travels about the room. The sound of light, it was thought, recalls the breathing of priests. The manner of the embers: this attracts horseflies and black ants. Burnt sackcloth appears to prefer hornets. All the mornings now are cold enough for wool.

Camastro, by some accounts, was pronounced with rocks in the mouth. It took the shape of a cage. In Spain, a bit later—the hinge, like the skin, painted yellow or white. As distinct from *camastro*, or *wicked bed,* which faced west and was composed of bones.

Jewish beds, in the New World, often faced east. The patterns of blood were understood in several ways. Spots a hand's-breadth apart, for instance, meant hatchets. Crosses meant wolves, just as you would guess. Or the throats, I suppose, of bride and groom—as logic might oblige some mention of a son.

The Gothic style, at tragic moments, stands on ceremony. I regret this. Sometimes it omits the box ornament and singe holes, however, as well as more ungainly traits. This example suggests a pile of knives. The legs, from the orphanage, and the slats, from the hospital, and the canopy—which is not the color, quite, of the wallpaper in my daughters' room.

My mother's will—it was silent on the subject. Rather like—you might indulge me—my father's will. If not the column, lying on its side, here outside the house. Decorum asks that I ignore the grass, burning gracefully from back to front. Or from door to gate, as across other American lawns. True, widows' wills a century ago—these may seem more amply despairing. This one includes a preamble that explains the frame as the form of a man. And portraits of the sickroom, a gas lamp—or just a hat and a rope—evident in the mirror.

The parable of the bed—were we to have it, that is. A carcass, in this case, would be a great success for us. Much in the manner of tongues nailed to a town. To corrupt an old phrase. The parable of the gown—a nightdress, in point of fact—presents various tales of failure. The wife dyed the garment. She wound a cord around the stick. A length of wool, rent, covered the floor. The litters—sometimes called scrolls—used mule hides in those days. Some funerary discourse favors kidskin, which may deprive the narratives of decapitation, among other insults. Bed etiquette, in such documents, forbids the kind of cloth I hold before you now. Whereas blankets and quilts sewn of limbs— these seem commonplace figures in folklore. Were your sister's things quiet and fine? Well, perhaps not, but the carts were—far from the towns, rolling over the hill. The spires always found the family behind the trees, tiny as they were. But what a pity about the soldiers' rings. Bits of their skin, charred, or imprinted with round marks, were pinned to the walls. The burning bed, in this blue house, was a simpler affair— the cross-stitch lost, on the husband's side, and the cuff at the rail, on the wife's. The bodies lay east to west. The latch was black, at last.

TEN

The hunt commences in a hollow or copse. A parlor, a yard, a lawn—these are for other occasions. *Grave*, given the hidden children, seems the most common variation. It requires five bones, paint or lye, and a figure in the distance. It is akin to *church windows*, despite the gate, and to *wolf*, despite the bats. In the former, the killer blinds at a barn wall. In the latter, a barn burns down.

Now there is ample view of the animals.

Branks, in which the partners quarrel—this is for the parlor. Hatpins—especially those foreign in design—have something of a ceremonial function here. This is less true of ruined broomsticks. The draw spoils, at length. The windows lose the blue roofs in the afternoon.

Poor Eleanor falls from favor by the end of the century. A later variation requires a hedgerow—and poison for the vermin. The forms, from above, may suggest graves, though daughters will also do. Orphans on the lawn—not to mention pitchforks—invite greater complications, especially at night.

Other animals die behind a schoolhouse.

The hunt commences in a hollow or copse. Cuts are drawn from wooden boxes—red or brown, as per local practice. The shapes in the dirt may suggest a different game, with rocks in place of the faces. *Grave* seems better suited to a hayfield. It is akin to *church windows*, despite the carriage tracks, and to *wolf*, despite the rows of claws on the wall. In the former, the girl waits at a door. In the latter, she closes her eyes and dies.

HOUSEPOST, MALE FIGURE

I.

The Tudor has a hidden room, or two hidden rooms, or three, through a crawlspace or a trapdoor, or behind the pantry wall—where the youngest son was found eight days later. The Georgian is a girls' school, with rifles on the lawn, or an orphanage, its upper stories destroyed during the war, the flesh of the attendant evident on the walk. The Cape is painted gray, and is famous for ladies in distress, carrying themselves down the stairs, and from window to window, facing Bird Road or Lion Drive or Red Lane, or facing the Cape next door, painted gray.

In Daniel and Susanna, the house is said to resemble a person—though you may find such comparisons embarrassing. And the city is a town, in fact. Shall we recall that the strangers—beyond the garden, at the

wall—are enamored of the woman? That they wait—
that is to say—for the man's wife?

The Victorian hides a bent hat and fourteen
knives—come watch Mother cutting—and is set afire by
Father, whom you can see between the trees. The Greek
Revival appears in a county almanac, absent the holiday
objects, and the gentleman's name, and the suitcase in
the nursery. The Colonial has a room for mutes, off the
entrance hall and through the study, or through the
sitting room and down one hallway and then another,
the latter terribly black, with a window giving onto a
courtyard—where the thief, having fallen from the roof,
dies during the night.

In our house: there are ten windows on the ground
floor.

I would prefer to exclude the two in the front room,
however, as they are pine-framed, unlike the others,
with drapery in an unpleasant shade of blue. I would
prefer to exclude, as well, the foyer window, from which
I once saw my wife embrace a rival of mine. And I would
prefer to exclude the powder room altogether—simply
as a demonstration of decorum.

The storm windows and the screens: these are rather in disrepair.

The lake window, as we would refer to it—though the house, of course, faces neither a lake nor a pond, nor even a creek, a fork, a stream—had been governed, for a time, by a curious assemblage of hinges, several of which suggested claws.

The objects on the windowsill: I suppose they were carried off—once and for all—by the wind.

It is more satisfactory in this corner of the house, at the bow window—especially in the morning, in spring, notwithstanding those occasions when the light makes grave shapes on the tabletop.

The panes in the middle row, left and center: they cracked last January and shattered in March.

The low windows along the dining room wall, three of them, each roughly one foot square, resemble leper windows, or so I used to think, having seen renderings of these in this book or that—likely something of my father's.

Transom windows and fanlights: these you will see in other houses.

The pantry window—dark glass, after the fashion of so-called blood windows, the field red and the details green, animals and houses, or houses and animals—was eventually painted shut.

The judas, I should probably add, was strangely placed—off-center, in any case, and a bit too high. It had been hidden, in the beginning, behind a grim little contraption, rather box-like in design, with six ordinary rivets, perhaps seven, perhaps eight, some smaller than others—a hook and a wire at the top, and a broken lever at the bottom.

The deadbolt was poor. It failed, shall we say, one February afternoon. The door was removed the following summer, incidentally—beetles of some species having taken to the frame.

A typical Colonial door has six panels, four rails, and two stiles.

Exterior: the letterbox, vertical or horizontal. The former appears in the hanging, or hinge, stile. The latter appears in the cross rail. Interior: the muntin, center and upper. This is for a name, in some houses. One abandons a nail there—or perhaps one's daughter does.

The rattling of a door, at this hour, may recall a certain boyhood story.

The floor plan of the Jackson house, on New Street, in Bethlehem, Pennsylvania—built 1838; restored 1914; destroyed, by fire, 1979—indicates, among other things, a narrow staircase, a narrow hallway, and four bedrooms, one drawn without windows or a door.

Some Colonial doors have four panels, three rails, and a long gash in the shutting stile.

Interior: the doorknob, enamel or wood. The former is usually white. The latter is blue, as per custom, on the occasion of a great disgrace. Exterior: thumb latch, pull, and plate. One expects cast-iron or brass. Rust, in this instance, finds its way to the numbers, top rail.

The dowels will warp by next fall.

The door was painted red one year, to match the back door, and brown another—some months after a storm. The hinges were nickel-plated. The copper doorstop was more unfortunate, I thought, than the little silver hook.

———

And I suppose that, after all, *spyhole* might have sufficed. It measured less than a quarter-inch across—more a puncture, as it were, than a proper hole. Or, at this distance, a simple yellow spot, on account of the porch light. And then a simple black spot, when the porch light went out.

In the foyer: a walnut floor. The cracks near the door create a triangular pattern. There are water scars at the foot of the stairs.

I scrape cobwebs from the baseboards with a dull knife.

Church oak, in folklore, bleeds every evening. And red oak, I notice, creaks quite modestly—at least in the rear hallway, early in the afternoon.

The object discovered beneath the floorboards, often something of the mother's, is a separate affair, a ghastlier matter for later on.

I prefer steel wool and turpentine for certain stains.

On the stairs: Axminster, six years old.

I stand on the landing—in an attitude of embarrassment—and then retreat to our room.

On the floor of the bedchamber or the corridor or

the inner parlor—in Thornton, during the war—the father dressed the daughters for their coffins.

Church oak, burning, recalls the sound of a stricken man. Or, by other accounts, the sound of a burning animal or a coffin bell.

I clean the ceilings with rags—remnants of bed-sheets, for the most part, and sleeves torn from white shirts—or with a wire brush.

In the guest room: Wilton broadloom, cut pile. A wooden pistol—in the form of a horse—sits in the far corner. Perhaps these are carpet beetles vanishing beneath the cabinet.

I count footsteps in the hallway.

In the country house—outside Lawton or Marion—they measured the dimensions of a body in repose, a body in distress, a body in agony, and marked the floor accordingly.

Some Colonial floor plans trace the progress of the body—or, put a different way, the path of the wife from room to room to room, and then down the stairs, and from the stairs to the door.

———

Sounds in the house: foyer and front hallway. I list them from left to right. I open and close all the drawers. The rain, the sound of the rain—this makes me afraid. The lock, I like to think—and now the teeth of the key; the latch—is rather less sad than the man standing on the porch, his umbrella a bit too red. But we prefer the wind, in any case, early in the morning—do we not? And the commotion in the trees, the curtains in May and June.

Were she to return: I imagine the sound as a narrow column, as a metal box, as a border of cloth.

Sounds in the house: front room and side hallway. Were you to adopt a posture of repose, supine on the brown chaise, say, at five o'clock in the afternoon, the door—across from the brickwork and the vitrine— might offer of itself one small corner and three curious noises. Or the contours of some other report—a hammer in an attic, and now an animal in a yard—were you to find yourself just west of the end table and just east of the fire screen, at eight o'clock in the evening, having fallen to your knees.

———

In our room: the curtains displayed faint stripes, a herringbone pattern, and a formation of birds—doomed, by the look of them.

The stain at the hem was an unseemly green.

Is it true that the Rowan bride—in a stone house, one hundred years ago—named her rooms for former suitors?

The deacons—in Eaton and Marion, but sometimes in Harrow as well—would arrange the shades in various ways, indicating contagion, danger, alarm, and so on. Whereas the strangler would hide behind the curtains, or within them, before crossing to the bedroom door.

In the hallway: the blinds made frightening sounds at night. They were wooden—maple, I expect, or elm. But dark brown is all I can recall.

The cord wound around a brass cleat.

The curtain and rod, the shade and ring—perhaps such figures are taken, in one tradition or another, as emblems of betrayal.

The wives—in Putnam and Whitebriar, and in Newbury and Bratton and Pike Fork—would open the drapes just so, and for only a moment, or two, or for an hour in the afternoon, and then close them, indicating a day of the week, a time of day, a location.

In the child's room: one curtain split lengthwise, along a pleat or a crease. The other, I gather, caught in the window and tore.

They were replaced with shutters, painted white.

Iron screens, detailed with human forms, their faces turned away—these were placed in the window frames of convent sickrooms and hospital morgues.

The daughters—in Thornton, during the war—would tie the curtains back, disclosing a skull on the windowsill. The maids took the curtains down in due course, carried them to the bed, addressed them with shears and a brush, and then set them atop the daughters' coffins.

Shadows in the house: bedrooms, master and guest. The first, on a curtain, a white curtain, suggests a ripsaw. Or, more sensibly, a crooked hand. The pine tree is the culprit, I take it, in conjunction with the wind. Or some aspect of the ladder—which will fall, in any case, before long. The second, on a bed, slants rather handsomely—until the door closes.

My form on the wall: it now assumes a more gruesome shape.

Shadows in the house: child's room. Were you to cross from the door at eight o'clock in the morning, in fall, the dormer window, to your left, might appear entirely black, at least for a moment. Were you to cross from the door at noon, however, and pause at the wardrobe, the shadows might contrive to remove from view one column, several trees—oak trees, I believe—and the name of the road.

The wagon at the hanging: this is no longer on the wall. And now we have the rats and the ants and the way the door sticks, even in winter. That makes up a day. But what about those nights when the shade is made to produce a sound like this one? All those lovely worries in the hallway, and the wire on the platter. As the hour passes. Or wears on, to be precise, until the lights go out.

The colors may recall the walls of your childhood room.

Wall hornets, in cathedrals, would conceal murals and the like—and were, on occasion, mistaken for inscriptions. But elsewhere, in a brown house, years later, there were only rows of coats in an entrance hall.

I touch it five times, the line on the wall—just west of the sconce and just east of the door. On the other side of which, yes, one's wife stands in her nighttime attire.

In the photographs from that year: you can see the son at the window, but never the daughter.

I count again the number of nails, up and down. The banister flatters the paneling, as the molding flatters the frame. The wallpaper has a dark border, the vines disguising the animals.

In castles, perhaps, bones were stacked to build walls—atop which you might see crosses, painted black to resemble those figurines once stationed at table in place of departed fathers.

A sledgehammer and a crowbar will do quite nicely in removing a bedroom wall.

The clock atop the lowboy: this has a skeleton dial. The mirror cuts the door in two. Do you imagine someone in the house? And now one anchor follows another, a little drawing on a shelf. Or a knife and a knife, and then a ruined hat. But this is foolish of me. I know that—I do. Take away the shade, after all, and we have nine panes, the socket, the channel, and the stop.

II.

As a child, as a boy: I was distracted, shall we say, by several forms on a wall. There were squares, a series of them, in four colors, maybe five. I imagined these to be houses, naturally, or rooms, a plain arrangement of rooms, the doors just out of view.

Or, on occasion, pillars in a row. Or a pillar, a long hallway, a staircase. The last, I grant you, may require some elaboration. I was small and still. It was winter. One line was brown, very brown. After an hour, or two, at six o'clock, or seven, my father would carry me out.

The sound was terribly bright, I thought. Though I suppose I was alone with this notion. He made shapes in the air with his hand—spot under spot. The next room was blue. My nightshirt was white—the color, perhaps, of your own childhood attire.

———

Or black, rather, and at nine o'clock. I was frightened, as you will gather from the timbre of my voice. I would find her crying—at the back door, and at the staircase. Touch your finger to the hem of your trousers or skirt— that is another sound altogether, is it not?

The finial was dull, or chipped, or missing—I can no longer recall. And the banister, the style of it—this is of little consequence now. I should note, instead, my height at age eight. And that the objects sat on the landing at a bit of a slant, and then fell down.

III.

The first story begins with the woman, or with the two of them, the man and the woman, in a town, a house afire at the end of a road. Or with a family in another town, far from this one. The widow is sometimes called a relict. The blind son is Edward or William or John. The father is always the father. There he is, crossing the lawn. How I wish we could save him before morning. The second story begins in the maid's chambers, but concludes in the sitting room. A child—the son—is decapitated by a portrait. His mother's, in one version—a fairy tale. A soldier's, in another—a romance.

In Matthew, the house is a dead bird or a box of thorns. But parables are not always the same as lies. Your dictionary calls them stories, but these we can see behind the child. All right—let us put it a different way. The man returns in the morning. He stands at the window. The woman departs in the afternoon.

In the third story, the child lights a candle on the anniversary of his mother's death. But the candle topples during the night, and the flame finds the drapery, one corner and then the next, traveling now with considerable haste to the edge of the rug, which catches, naturally, carrying the flame to the wall, to the door, to the foyer, and then up the stairs and along the hallway to a room—where a pair of shoes burns first, and then the nightstand, and the blanket and bedsheet, and the father asleep in the bed.

Animals, yard and road, 1848: fall. The birds ignore the birdhouse, a few pipes and a wire. Mauled house cat, north side. Three carriage accidents, south side. Field, 1871: fall. A man drowns ten rabbits in a stream. Town,

1887: fall. They cry a porcelain lion on a wooden platform, hickory or deal.

Were you to gather the blanket this way, and set it on a chair, in winter, in the sewing room or the sitting room—horses on the wall; a wolf on a shelf—or in one of the rooms named for a color—late in the afternoon, the light terrifically dim—it might conjure, finally, the form of your boyhood dog.

Animals in the walls, child's room, 1952: summer. The parakeets shriek for three days. Master bedroom, 1954: summer. The rats run from east to west, late at night, behind the headboard—walnut; a bend at the center; six feet across—and back again, from west to east, returning to the attic early in the morning.

New Street, 1858. Daniel Anderson: merchant (suit of clothes, burnt). Charles Barnett: gentleman (brick house, two horses). James Berger: surgeon ("My son kills moths under the awnings"). William Brown: caretaker ("It was my greatest unhappiness"). John Cole: unknown. Samuel Cole: unknown. Theodore Cole: unknown. Nathan Dixon: gentleman (frame house, horse and carriage). Herman Fine: trimmer (drawing of a city bridge, ball-peen hammer). Francis Hoffman: cordwainer (irregular pulse, weak heart). Edward Hunter: clerk ("My brothers fell that morning from the widow's walk"). Aaron Jackson: gentleman ("My father wore the horns"). Jacob Leach: watchmaker (hives, stitch, anemia, fever). Walter Moore: shut-in (house and lot, horse and carriage). Alexander Morton: slater (doll's head, hollow). William Munson: unknown. Thomas Nelson: unknown. John Nicholas: gentleman ("We were married in every town"). Bartholomew Ott: merchant ("I once received letters like these"). Richard Pollard: coffinmaker (catalog of animals, red umbrella). Isaac Rice: driver (jaundice, palsy, blindness, stroke). Arthur Ritter: clergyman (cabinet of English linen, revolver). George Sexton: lawyer (house and lot, two horses and carriage). Timothy Skinner: tailor (chestnut secretary, burnt). Timothy Skinner, Jr.: unknown. Edward Todd: constable ("Charlotte won my heart"). Peter Turnbull: dyer ("If only I had hastened home"). Frederick Twitchell: clerk (lesions, bleeding, pleurisy, seizure). John Wilton: gentleman (two place-settings, garden spade).

———

Household calamities, 1863: spring and summer. An attic collapses under cannon fire. Lightning destroys a porch awning, a Dutch door, a wedding trellis. A cyclone destroys eight chimneys and a balcony. (Mr. Porter, the lodger, removes to the cellar with a fowling piece, a flannel hat, a crate of dirt, and a pasteboard face.)

How to survive a household fire, 1905: crawl to the door. Or remain in place. Or hang a white bedsheet from the window—and cry out your wife's name. Family disaster plan, 1926: three pages, in triplicate. Or four diagrams with broken lines. Or a map of the town, evacuation route in blue thread.

Household accidents, 1957: fall and winter. They carry the father to an empty room, loosen his collar and necktie, cover the wound. An icicle finds the child's left eye—and then the right. Collapsed ladder, soldier. Four poisonings, boys. Stove fires, various. (Mrs. Gray, the neighbor, drives an automobile onto the lawn, and then onto the walk, and then into the front room.)

Portrait of Albert Post, 1864. A man in a uniform stands before a field tent. Second Lieutenant, 45th Regiment, Pennsylvania Infantry. (He dies eight years later.)

Execution of the Bridegroom, 1868. A man in a tailcoat stands before a house. The door is thought to recall a hood or shroud, the windows—shuttered—crosses or closed eyes, and the steeples at the roofline a pair of horns. (The church burns to the ground in a subsequent painting.) *Execution of a Jew*, 1873. A man hangs—upside down, arms in chains—between two dogs. The beam is far darker than the posts, which are far darker than the cart. (The second panel depicts a row of houses on a road.)

One year passes for the family, and now another, town by town, door by door, room by room, despite the color of the bedclothes, and despite the objects, hers or his, or theirs—an old knife in a pail, if you like, and a wooden animal on a platter—beside the bed.

Diorama, 1959. An automobile, a felled tree, a visitor at the door. (He is without a proper hat or a suitable coat.) The house is brown, with yellow trim. There are ten rooms, a cellar, and an attic. The father, in a near corner—returning to, or retiring from, the foyer. ("I had hoped to fail more grandly.") The son hides behind the shed. (It can be sad in a yard, can it not?) Firewood and a scythe, a dog on the porch. There are chalk drawings on the cellar floor. A stranger, in a hallway chair—a mousetrap and a teakettle at his feet. ("I wore the room poorly.") The mother, evidently preparing to cry, turns away. (And what does she see?) There are three windows across, and open curtains. Wires, a lamppost, the daughter on the walk. (She carries an uncomely valise.) The street ends at a red fence.

IV.

Whereupon: I would repair from the landing to the hallway—it was rather narrow; a garment of some sort comes to mind, woolen, in the company of another object, a larger one, something copper or brass—at the end of which stood my bedroom door.

They believed me enamored of the color red, which may explain the blanket and the wallpaper and the lampshade, if not the configuration of items—mangled animals, at least as the shadows had it—on the windowsill.

Did you see, on certain evenings, your brother's face in the drapery? I would divide the ceiling at the wire, and then list all the letters in the names. I would find the seam in the carpet, and then subtract from ten, from seven, from five. But at what hour? The closet door, in this inventory, was a matter of no account.

How unfortunate, furthermore, the condition of the trinkets, shattered with a hammer—and the bedsheets, on the top shelf, ripped from end to end. I would disarrange the articles with great address, holding each one to my throat. The slant of light, I think, permits mention of the partition. Eightpenny nails lined the bottom shelf.

In the photograph, I was the child on the right, beside a stray mark, a mistake at the edge of the frame. I should like to recount, at this point, before I fall ill, or am overtaken by distraction or melancholy, how we lost the house—but I can no longer remember the story.

V.

The gun room has two doors, or three—compare the first, if you please, with the father's body—and a table painted gray. The parlor wallpaper, from afar, through the garden window, or as it appears in a photograph, torn out one afternoon from this book or that, or from the family album, and then marked in a number of places—with X's, unless these are crosses—seems to display a row of green lions and black hatchets, or perhaps a formation of brown towers around a blue lake.

The conduct book describes a wooden house on a creek, all the doors and windows nailed shut. The household almanac describes a stone house, a cottage, the blind son in bed. The marriage manual describes a Colonial house, where the maid prepares a room for Mrs. Hand, a friend from town.

The bedrooms—four small disappointments, according to the father—display photographs in chrome frames, or silver ones, and collections of broken objects. The dining room has a drop-leaf table—a spoon clicks against the man's tooth; the woman chokes to death on a pheasant bone—and a sideboard with a false drawer. The powder room takes its name from an eighteenth-century chamber—but here the wig is covered with blood, and falls to the floor. The hidden room—off the front hallway, or beyond the rear staircase, or behind the pantry wall—has a trapdoor, from which hangs a ladder to the cellar.

In the cellar: a pull saw and a hasp, a jack plane, a wrecking bar, and a claw hammer. A tin contains a cap screw and a razor blade. A jar contains the remains of a carpet beetle.

I dismantle the chairs and place all the parts in a crate. I station the broom beside the garden spade.

The killer in the cellar, in folklore, is discovered by a mute child. The prisoner in the cellar survives a fire or a storm—but is later mauled by wolves.

There were fleas last year, and squirrels the year before that.

The foundation plan of the Burrows house, on Market Street, in Durham, Pennsylvania—built 1875; sold 1878; destroyed, by flood, 1914—indicates, upper right, a furnace room, divided in two, and a disappearing staircase.

In the attic: a stump doll, a child's rifle, a wig on a wooden peg. Grandmother's hat-stands—the initials in cursive—are set out on a metal ledge. A suitcase contains five nightdresses and a carriage bolt.

There is a mark on the doorpost, in pencil, forty-one inches from the floor.

Mannikins—Mary Casket and John Coffin—would hang from the rafters in Colonial attics. Dollhouses, in Victorian attics, were sometimes arranged to form foreign towns—and, it turns out, to capture bats.

I place the poison in each corner. I find the bodies behind the door—that morning or afternoon, or by the end of the week.

The cross section of the Grimes house, on Oak Road, in Thornton, Pennsylvania—built 1906; sold 1938; torn down 1939—indicates, among other things, an attic door, ajar, and blackout at a ridge vent.

I would prefer a dragon beam, actually, fractured or otherwise, if not jack rafters and a scissor brace, or even queenposts on a tie beam, or hammerposts on a hammer beam, the purlins having been ravaged in the usual manner. But these elements, alas, occur elsewhere—a few doors away, or down a block, or over a hill and toward the river, crossing the bridge now into the next town.

————

The roof often appears a peculiar blue. At this distance, anyway—from the lawn and the walk. The dormers are somewhat darker.

Your standard roofing nail, nine gauge or ten, barbed, lands on the awning or on the garden path.

Slating: copper wire. Shingle: cut-iron or steel.

Is it true that the mansard roof was named for the form of Mansart's coffin?

But now we are north of the boy.

Poor boys fall from chimneys only in the morning, according to that old saying—just as a gentleman drowns only at night. Either way, a windstorm next August will carry off the neighbor's weathervane.

I paint the eaves and doorframes every five years. I have twice replaced the flashing at the ridge.

The shakes are cedar or pine or cypress, hand-split and stained.

Pitch: 12/12.

The gambrel roof was named for the gambrel stick—bent like a horse's leg, and from which butchers would hang dead animals.

Lightning strikes the ladder, several rungs down.

My father's house, on New Street, in Bethlehem,

Pennsylvania—which I visited as a child, in 1969—was a brown Colonial with four columns, dentil molding, and a widow's walk.

The cornice vents attract various insects—crickets, termites, flies.

Flat wire: one foot square. Single bead: soldered.

And now we find a cat's tail near the downspout.

The gable roof was named for the gable wall—brick, in this case, with an ornament on the door.

From above, the man on the roof—just east of the dormers; prone—may appear a branch or a pitchfork, or perhaps a tiny gap in the valley.

Tulips are rooms in red blood. Have I mistaken the phrase? Horsetail grows in the yard. You weed and you weed, but in it creeps. *Lawn* also refers to a linen of some sort—and *plat,* at one time, referred to the shape of a blade. Imagine a dagger or an ax, or those swords designed to resemble bodies. Women of a certain station, I once read, were not to be seen in the presence of knives. And so the ancients would place their artifacts at the doorpost, and take away on a glass plate a portion of the offering.

―――――

The porch light: this scatters the cats. I sweep the patio every two weeks, and clean it with bleach in summer and fall. The wind in the pickets, I should think, terrifies the mice. But now I have lost the sun again. A squirrel drowns one Monday in a flowerpot. I bait the traps with meat, and cut the branches along the path. I trip—you see?—on the last step.

The object nailed to the tree: something small and wooden, but not a doll.

The Rowan children would feign death on the doorstep of the first house; and in the yard of the second house, before a shed and a hedgerow; and in a field of weeds beyond the third house, next to a barn, the name and the hex sign upside down.

A newspaper account describes a boy of five, caught beneath a maple gate for sixteen hours—outside the Milton house, on Bird Road, in Whitebriar, Pennsylvania, 1953.

In folklore, the orphans cross one road and then another—having traveled due south for three days, or perhaps four; and having discovered a breach in the greenery; and having surmounted a low wall or fence—arriving at your door in the middle of the night.

The trap in the crocus patch: this breaks the rat's neck.

The patio: two columns, a lantern, and a wrought-iron bench. Doll parts are arranged on the lawn. A few of the taller trees—these are diseased. Needle blight, is it not? I water the annuals in the afternoon. The dog pursues the birds quite ruefully, it seems to me, falling just before the porch door. I set the tacks on rags and cover them with ash.

The doorframe disappoints the wall, as the wall disappoints the floor. The mullions divide the yard into nine portions. But *portions*—or, if you like, *portion*—is an unlovely word. *Guest* and *host*, for their part, issue from the same root—*ghostis.* Which means *stranger, villain, enemy*—though naturally I had believed it to mean *ghost.* And the figure in the corner, lower right, is neither my daughter nor her hat, but just a paper bag in the grass.

On the north side: the fence is six feet high, board on board, posts four on center. The pickets are in the Gothic style. On the south side: the fence is four feet high, open-picket with three-inch spacing, posts eight on center, rails at the top and at the bottom.

You would be forgiven, however, for mistaking a certain post—on at least one occasion, in the rain—for the form of a woman. While the split rail—hanging at this angle—often puts me in mind of a skeleton on a wall.

The gatepost, in our case, rotted first.

A gate, absent a lock, may be understood as—in legal parlance—a place of danger. The creaking of metal gates—this, I like to think, was the great eighteenth-century sound. Just as the great nineteenth-century sound was the burning house.

She would kneel here with the shears.

On the west side: the hedgerow is six feet high. The wasps keep mostly to the rockery—beyond the flowerbed, the creeping Jenny, and the child's things. Burdock—also known as cuckold's dock, as it happens—grows more beautifully, it is safe to assume, outside other houses.

I cannot abide a column overgrown with vines.

On the east side: the garden wall is five feet high, brick in a standard configuration, flush cut. The child found mice there from time to time. The bats prefer the latticework, the balcony, the gutters. The border plants burn or freeze, as the case may be.

I am displeased by the pine trees, by their location and arrangement, and by the manner of the shadows thrown across the lawn. A section of the path is hidden behind the firewood. The stakes are placed every three feet, from the gatepost to the cellar doors.

The deed, duly executed in the month of November, covenants that the party of the first part has neither suffered nor wept, walking the lot haltingly, from a corner formed by hazels, around said curve, thence north 86 degrees, 44 minutes, 29 seconds, a distance of fifty feet to a point or site of conclusion on the eastern line.

On the street map: a creek, a park, a boulevard.

The survey refers to a lane rather than an alleyway. A revised version, dated two days later, corrects this— but mistakes several letters in my name.

Some Colonial maps are adorned with bridal inscriptions or memorial borders. I gather, however, that diagrams of fire are rare even in the earliest specimens.

Lot: 7. Block: 23.

Red arrows—and the letter P, reversed—mark the iron rods, capped, that appear as zeros in various places.

Radial, north side: 118 feet. Radial, south side: 125 feet.

A rood, in England, is a quarter acre—but may evoke, in the New World, animals in the kill. The sky is dead leaf or king's yellow or burnt lake—at least as the field books have it.

The survey of the Burton property, on Court Street, in Germantown, Pennsylvania—purchased 1930; abandoned 1931—indicates, at the bottom of a pond, a treeline and a tiny folly.

The Gunter's chain has one hundred links, steel wire. The choke is a brass device—akin, in certain depictions, to a compass—trampled in the grass, or lost one morning in a forest. The dials sometimes resemble headless birds.

Tract: 8. District: 16.

I mark a large square in the garden, its western edge ten feet from the property line.

Some Colonial maps display rows of daggers, for fenceposts, and rows of cannons, for houses. The bell tower is often replaced with a list of solemn phrases.

On the county map: a mountain range, a river and a bridge, a turnpike.

The survey places my wife's name beside mine. The name of the town appears just above a signature and a date, and just below a single black stroke.

ADULTERIUM

ONE

Decline implies a distant relation. Better this, you know, than Henry or Edward. Poor John is all alone on the porch. Another name is written out, in black ink, on the headboard and on the bedroom wall. Butcher is our favorite shade of blue. *Quietly*, on the other hand, offers a view of the husband from the house. In this case, the victim sits in three parts. A clattered bone is homelier than a drowned wagon. The sticks, such as they are, appear at a peculiar angle. The dead card is read at the garden wall.

The ashpit attracts finches rather than bats, but the housecoat catches fire anyway.

Long affliction is worse, of course, in August. The lawn is brown, spoiling things every morning. The afternoon begins with Miss Milligan in a corner room. It concludes with stewed tripe, or with aspic and a knuckle of veal.

Our house seems meager between the trees.

Wasting, for near relations, offers little scenic detail. In this case, a souvenir cracks in two. The blade is the face and the haft the body proper. It follows, often, that the ladies wait at a train station. *As a matter of course* implies the nighttime attire. The shift exhibits a chain-stitch, worn on the wrong side. Killdeer and sparrows are found in the piano. Laurel, it appears, cannot come down after all. We are so sorry to hear about Dorothy and Anne. Another name is written out, in black ink, on the back of the attic door.

A staircase will do for the swoonings.

TWO

The knife recurs as a figure in certain rooms. Take the parlor, where the matron, aflame, parts the drapes—and the bedroom, where brown ants cover the haft.

Have a better look.

The spine, despite its color, whatever this may be—I imagine you find the light as dim as I—dates the item. The break remains the break—in halves, to the left of the letters. The pike hides the rust very nicely.

Your carving articles, years ago, might include a little brass hook, this to remove the eyes. A scullion would address the red tables. An abigail would attire the girls, were there any. These cleavers, of the kind we were accustomed to in childhood, if more ornate, had been devised for cadavers, in fact. Pluck its feathers, they say, and a butcherbird resembles a blade. Hold it this way and it resembles a hand aslant. But skinning implements have no place in a good home, have they? The demeanor of these, I submit, and of the leavings, to say nothing of the town steeples—evident now at the near window—settles the question.

Flay, in any case, once meant *bed*, as in a ditch or a trench, or on a wide green lawn one summer afternoon—given the terms of the early American lexicon.

While *stab* would prevail on the more suitable occasions.

At the time of our murder, reader, a knife might display the victim's name. This was less the habit later in the century. Messages of other kinds, engraved on the male side, were customary in some marriages. The effect upon the heart, as distinct from the throat, to cite only two bodily objects, was certainly great—but was usually described in unfortunate ways. The letter V as arrow, in one view. In another, the letter L as pistol or gibbet. Immurement of this sort, whatever the text, came to seem rather too mannered a practice.

The man stands in the corridor, the woman at the top of the stairs.

The color changes at the ridge—toward the wood now, once and for all. Blue often implies something human. Black letters, as these, to the left of the emblem, contrive to escape harm.

Surgical instruments—in a hemlock box, in a bridget—would sometimes assume unusual forms. They were likely to split, grips of this variety—stag instead of hickory or larch. Ivory—forgive me the handprints and the rats, the late hour—was always taken down first, the carts dashed with pitch. The bone saw would say the boy's name. Horn saws would bloom in the road. But some maps favor exaggeration, do they not? From above, the houses seem to bleed. These versions, rivets pitted brown, were reserved for oxen—wounded in the straw, or lost—and these, with nickel-plated teeth, for cuckolds and Jews. Another tale, offering the latter facts more amply, and less dully, notes the shape of the rope in the dayroom.

If death is a room, as one conception has it, then where is the family? Let us wait in a safe place and consider this. Are the doors an argument for ornament? Doubtless they are said to resemble sad men. The route to the bureau, I suspect, is just as you remember it. Do excuse the collars—or excise them. Can we conclude that the bed is properly dressed? See how the knife lies there, at this angle, in lieu of you.

In the history of adultery, women cross all morning, east to west, as in the parable of the gown: a murderer left—in the parlance—for dead, without further confession, post after post after post. In the history of adultery, women cross from this corner to that, in gowns, as in the parable of the copse, where a body is found—broken, in one description; dead, in another— though suddenly the origins of *corpse* seem in order, or at least preferable, post after post after post, the other houses without a sound. In the history of adultery, men fall on the lawn, and at the gate, one by one, or they kneel, merely, among a woman's things, as in the parable of the house, where the room faces south, and where the husband finds the wife.

See how the drapes disclose the road.

The declining hour, I can confide, is always lonely, a fact that returns us to the terms of the town—but I ought not speak so often of grief.

Manners for mourners differed somewhat in the country, where a dinner-setting might include, to the left of the strop, a jar of hearts. A child's knives should sit crosswise. A white plate should conceal a dark card. Have they measured as yet the length of the carcass? Grouse, in bruises, to use the local phrase, was acceptable on these occasions. Pox hen, gutted and trussed—or potted—was not. The decorum of boys, as to the body, and in the event of slaughter, for that matter—the sheep at the rail, if not the goats—was a lesser concern.

There they were, in bleak attire.

A flaying blade appears as ornament in certain documents, and also as the sign of Saint Bartholomew—flayed alive, by all accounts, and now drawn without a face.

In some later cases, furthermore, the murderer would engrave the blade with a particular figure. A spire meant the left eye, and a lance the right. A pitchfork or an orphan pin—one of these, I believe, meant the heart. Organ knives were designed for the windpipe, the lungs, the intestines, and so on. While the bed knife—sometimes called a pale or a picket, after the fashion of the more lavish axes—was an indication of shame, in every case. Hold it this way, at night, and it resembles the neck. Have the shadows as you prefer them. The maul sword, for the cleaving of limbs, was said to die as we do. A strange notion, that, given the location of the gouge—rather green from across the room—and given the hilt in the light.

The ridge is blue, like the wound—but easy to mistake for a stain. A black emblem, to the left of the fault, shows the town's arms and, in the background, a pattern of animals. The spine reflects a portion of flesh.

The man stands at the window, the woman at the bed.

A knife box of the period—in locust or elm—might display the family name. Calfskin would conceal the nails. Hinges of the spike type—shot copper instead of low brass—were believed to carry plague. Is ours without a proper lock? It might sit atop a red table, near the Queen Anne chairs. Open, it might resemble an urn. There were usually two, in those days, side by side—unhappy as that sounds. The wrought-iron rings were another great regret. While battle-scabbards were often missing from the narratives altogether—despite the matter of the beadle and the chambermaid, stabbed at last in a church tower.

The family is far away. Ornament, according to one argument, portends death. And bedposts of this kind, I suspect, are better suited to other rooms. Do you approve of the birds in the bureau drawer? The wool presents a flaw all its own. The bedsheet is embroidered with hornets—or spotted with blood. The gown is torn. Does the knife hide politely? Brown ants cover the hands, the outline traced with dye.

THREE

Conveyance of the remains: in coffins.

These are adorned with various forms. The likeness of a child—most notably—or an overturned rowboat. The hanging features a three-legged mare, which gives way, in later examples, to a simpler figure.

The drop, at Newgate, 1783.

Two posts and a crossbeam, a five-foot trap, and a scaffold covered with haircloth or drill. The veil always acquits itself quite well. Ox-carts travel hither and yon.

A balcony gallows may help dignify things a bit, despite the maulings in the courtyard.

A roadside gibbet, for its part, makes little accommodation for the sounds in a house.

The long drop, at Lincoln, 1872.

This effects a broken neck, yes. Or, as in the hangings of—among others—Mr. Adams and Mrs. Brown, decapitation. Shrikes may imply a later occasion in a summer month.

But to retrieve ourselves from distraction, please.

The coffins: four across.

Blue is appropriate for a battle or a strangling, though a fire is more likely. A drowning, in this case, requires clouts at the partition. A betrayal requires an elm floor, rotted through.

The Murder Act of 1752 excludes the carriage and the roofline.

Mr. Twitchell—having stabbed to death Mrs. Twitchell—hangs at Penton in June. The hood is a white cap, in fact, with three defects. The dissection is performed at Surgeons' Hall.

There follows a quiet fall on a gravel walk.

The Anatomy Act of 1830 excludes the attendants, two and two.

The steps—at Bristol, at Vickers, at Westgate—are painted red. At Hackett, the sexton stands at a rail. A ladder, by contrast, would imply a schoolroom or a barracks.

A winding-sheet would imply contagion, despite the burlap sacks at the chapel wall.

The coffins: on the lawn.

These are adorned with various forms. The likeness of a child—divided lengthwise—or an overturned rowboat. The inscriptions, in cursive, list the hour and the year, and then explain the arrangement of graves.

FOUR

The *mother* gives way, in due course, to a red morris—so named for the disposition of steeples beyond the burial mound, or for the absence of the man's arms—and then to a blue room. The *son*, the first one, hidden inside a cabinet or a bureau, something small and ordinary, or—less likely—a Queen Anne wardrobe, is buried alive.

Perhaps January will allow for another accident on the balcony.

The coffin is for the boy, in all those old storybooks, and the casket for the man. The mortician, the barn wall, the mute swan—these pages are torn in an elegant way.

The *daughter*—disconsolate, contrary, stout—is without a portrait, save for the morgue drawing.

The lid of the coffin, at least on these occasions, is a walnut headboard or a pine door. A so-called griever's-knife endeavors to separate the relations from the remains.

December seems more sensible for a murder.

The *father* waits in the gravery—twitch grass and bracken, as it happens, outside the parish house, with animals collapsing in the background. The *son*, the last one—never mind the claims that the doorframes are composed of bones, or that the bier is a horse on four pickets—wears his brother's garments.

The coffin, lined with broadcloth or felt, sometimes contains poison for the worms. A surname appears at the bottom of the page—circled, but also crossed out.

FIVE

The common wasp measures roughly two hundred hertz. This is well below the frequency of, say, a human scream. Anderson compares the sound of a dying beetle with the sound of a dying fly. (The names of the families escape me at the moment.) The common bee, absent its wings, is somewhat higher in pitch. (Carpenter bees would swarm the porch in August.) The true katydid says "Katy did"—or, according to Scudder, "she did." The false katydid produces a different phrase altogether, something far more fretful. Wheeler concludes with the house ant and the rasp of a pantry door. Douglas prefers a hacksaw drawn across a tin can. (We found termites in the bedclothes one year.) A sixteenth note, poorly formed, may be said to resemble a pipe organ or a hornet. The children set their specimens on black pins.

———

Pritchard—or perhaps Hood—devises a sparrow trap with nine chambers. Miller lists several calls for geese and quail. But the illustrations, in Tilton's manual, show congregations of jays. Overleaf, grouse hang in a country town. (The door recalls ours, it seems to me.) The lonesome call—a pattern of four noises, according to Walker—can occur in a simple pit. A piano blind can imply a sad family story. (A shot bird makes a brown sound—or so I thought as a boy.) The hunter's command is "blood"—and now the spaniel endeavors to terrify the guests—or "dead bird." Evening grosbeaks are seen near the edge of the oaks, beyond the folly, in a row. Yellowhammers drop on the walk. The chains, on some occasions, approximate the timbre of a man's voice. A certain hex sign describes a child buried alive.

Ordinary breathing, for a boy, measures roughly ten decibels. Bedside crying, in winter, in a brick house, animals on the walls—roughly eighty. (The rag doll was without hands, I now recall.) A woman says "dear," or perhaps "door," and then two names—or perhaps only one. The action of a hinge, according to Dalton, falls between a shriek and a scream. Burns prefers a series of wails, all in the upper register. (The deadbolt was a dark color.) A father's sobbing, in a corridor and a stairwell, and then in a tiny room, second story, early in the evening—this may be mistaken for toppling objects or for the scraping of a fire grate. (My window faced the road.) Martin lists the rattlebox and the copper pot, but neglects the cat trapped in the attic. The children arrange the knives in three piles.

SIX

But how much lovelier had the wife worn, that evening or the next, the other item, which was quite white, after all, far whiter than the spot at the mouth or the lines of the husband's cuffs: the rest of his things, woolen by the look of them, trousers and the like, and an odd portion of cloth, folded over the chair. If, as I have been led to understand, *shroud* implies *groom* (the latter deriving from the former, or vice versa) rather than *dagger* (which is apparently without connection to *dowager*—but how I regret these grisly, inexpert approximations)—then, notwithstanding the corpse on the bier, whether hers or his, the body may imply, say, the contours of a hornbook or a nuptial bed, or it may, simply, fall.

SEVEN

The word *adultery* derives from *cry*—which calls to mind, certainly, the way the blanket folded back—and from *alter*, rather than *altar*, via *reave*. But I flatter myself that this provides a correct measure of evidence. Nor does the wood, worse still—Queen Anne at the bottom of the stairs; Martha Washington at the knife box, with a bonnet top and a pierced apron. The posts, don't you know, later became coffins, just as the headstones later became roads—even if *skulduggery* derives from neither *skull* nor *grave*. The latter, incidentally, is also the name of a town in Pennsylvania—where, as I fancy it, he was born; and where, as it now appears, they stopped—and the name of, more happily, an early children's game—bleach and stack the bones; carve the hearts in the dirt; place the mice inside.

I recall a pause of some sort.

Criminal conversation, as the common notion, and as the preferred legal term—*preferred* here a ruptured version of something finer, either hers or his, while *ruptured,* now that we have it, revives for me too keenly that awful fall—dates from the nineteenth century, in America at least, in a house in Pennsylvania, in a high bed, in—to contort the conceit further—a torn gown. If only it were, say, brass and wool, rather than four-poster and silk, and, say, embroidered hornets, rather than spotted blood—*to live with,* in the standard definition, or *to live on,* alone there at the top of the stairs. But the finial and the bed, remember, later became theirs, or, better still, were lost to us—a less noisome phrase, this, even if it neglects the fire. Evidently hearts once required a burnt deck, like heartsette, which added a wound, and like matrimony, for the lonely—but unlike blind girl, in which the hearts were marked out.

Were this a medical, rather than a marital, history—you might then excuse so conspicuous a series.

And what follows:

Miniatures sometimes left spaces in place of them. Or, more often, collections of figures, usually in blue dye. These could evoke other bodies, but were not always akin to surgical inscriptions of the day. Models of hearts appeared in wood, and then iron, and then gold. Or ormolu, depending upon the victim, as in the Hessian specimen. They were eventually chipped away for kindling or melted down for buckshot, but most hospital documents omit discussion of this.

Even the earliest primers compare the heart's shape to a fist or to a hand waving goodbye.

Matrimonial law, such as it was, and such as it obtained, in particular, at Hunt and Bonelawn and Cripplegate, among other towns less beguilingly named, required excision at the knuckle—one was made to kneel at the foot of the bed, to remove the ring; one was asked to present the family ax—or, in what was thought a more genteel tradition, a white cord at the throat. It was silk on certain occasions, wool on others, such as this one— tartan, say, bars of whatever sort—the rot of little concern here, I am beginning to think. The scarf and the gloves— terribly evident, still, as she had arrived late, or he had, a door there at the end of the corridor—were becoming, though not black, no, not in the way of the apron, painted something closer to gray, actually, or of the cannon, which was played with four hands on an embalming table.

She kept her rings in the knife box.

Scar letter, referring neither to the quaint habit of quotation apparent in some later argument—"I wear my hair in a scar"—nor to the sentiment that the dark shapes on a page resemble rows of scars, disappears from dictionaries in the nineteenth century. As does *horn*, incidentally, at least in the sense of *gallows*—the planks, let us imagine, emblazoned with names. The coffins— now, I cannot beg off altogether—were marked with charcoal, the chains displayed near the smallest figures, which may indicate a measure of affection, or, given what had befallen them—the description of the crime; the history of the malady; the form of the contagion—a term in the northern cell, notable at that time for its bone hooks and bronze grille, the former engraved with the prisoners' symbols, numbers, initials.

Absent, however, were matters of marriage and a house.

And the rest of the evidence retreats, as I do, from the bodies:

They were sometimes mistaken for bundles of cloth. Children sometimes left rats in place of them. Various sadnesses, if not bad weather, attended their arrival. Knives and rifles were found in the graves. Emblems, probably imprinted on the skin, were presented by way of explanation. Evidently they were akin to bridal inscriptions of the day—a hatchet on end; a musket aflame; a dagger pointing south.

But to liken these to the designs on the bedsheets, even were I to omit the blotches of red, indistinct at so great a distance anyway—this might effect too lavish a comparison.

Cuckoldry, my proper topic, introduces fewer such obstructions, as, in this case, we have a cleaver rather than a hat—*rather* does merit something further by now, deriving, if a bit circuitously, from *jackal*, and thus suggesting, among more familiar conceptions, those portraits of mauled boys—and faces painted on shutters, painted on doors, and, in the better houses, carved into walls. If only the wallpaper had offered as pleasing a diversion—or just a fabric like the gown's, with bleak little seams. The blanket, on the other hand, implies some custom of theirs, her garments set out in a precise way—matrimony, incidentally, once required widow's weeds and, by the nineteenth century, crosses of moths, pinned—or a brief event at the foot of the bed.

I recall the house, from the outside, at night.

The word *adultery* does not, in fact, derive from *cry*—just as you had suspected—and the town, I will concede, suitably antique, and quiet now, stands in lieu of another town, come what may, these stains—cheerfully small—on the blade of the paring knife. The ax-blade was steel on certain occasions, silver on others, depending upon the family—the face already engraved with the surname, and the notch perfectly burnt. The handles later became balusters, which later became posts, row after row after row, as in the preamble about the house—a spine on a white plate; a pile of toile clothing; a swarm of fleas in the evening—and the addendum about the bedroom.

EIGHT

But how much simpler to consider them from afar, from the door, say, or from the corridor and the stairs, the husband in particular, the next morning: examining locks, drawers, cabinets and the like, uncovering and covering, unfolding and folding, all the articles a darker color in a better light—as the wife turns this way. *Costume* comes to mind, preferable as it is to *vesture*, to *raiment*, to *disguise*, or to my own attire, for that matter, warp, weft, and so forth—though you may prefer her ermine collar, or a table of cropped collars in a funeral parlor, the choke-smock conjuring the body as a dressmaker's form, or as a diagram of red wounds, or as, more likely, a man in a cutaway, leaving a room.

NINE

I.

Perforation of the left atrium, and then the right, as occasioned by a ten-inch blade—this posits obvious complications. The introduction of said blade to the diaphragm (between the seventh and eighth ribs) or to the liver (already afflicted with dropsy, incidentally) would explain a break in the aorta. Passage through the lung (inferior lobe, left-side posterior) into the mitral valve (named for the bishop's hat, I gather) would explain apoplexy.

In the case of knitting needles, a pair of these, clutched in the customary way—let us imagine a wound somewhat less shapely.

The hospitals favor blocked columns, skew arches, brick. Crow steps are always something of a surprise.

The city examples, modest as they are, are most notable for their nailhead molding. The county examples have black doors.

If the surgical theater is found on the north side, and the boys' ward on the south—better, then, to neglect the location of the litter.

The awl is for soldiers rather than spinsters. A hairpin sits between a lancet and a matchbox, just above the bleeding bowl.

A reflection will show the victim in repose.

A wooden version, a model, with the appropriate veins and chambers painted various colors, or stuck with tacks—this accounts for the fire.

To repair a hole in the heart, or septal defect, of the type common in children, first determine the site of incision (the sternum seems agreeable) and mark it. Cut accordingly. If the lines remind you of pickets, or of wire, or of your wife's fingers—look away. Rupture of the heart, or heartbreak (to use the Victorian term), requires sawdust and longcloth—though mortification of the organs usually indicates a different complaint.

Transfixion (atrial, through the anterior wall, the tendon well hidden—or tracheal, at the first ring) requires a clean white smock. Extract the blade posthaste. Suture the wound with silver rather than catgut or silk. Expect death within ten days.

Sickroom decoration, pertaining especially to the selection of curtains—the depictions vary by circumstance. On Union Avenue, in an upper room. On Broad Street, across from cannons, at the end of a corridor. On New Street, in a house with a blue roof, or a red one, the rot a bit of a pity.

Muslin is more becoming than wool, notwithstanding the examples at hand.

Carpets stain nicely in spring.

Pearl-ash and lime restore scorched linen—and poison the dog.

The affliction dictates the location of the children. At the fire irons for grippe, for falling sickness, for Mother's consumption. At the door, which is shut, for daggers. The color of the curtains dictates the color of the wood. Or vice versa—as moths cover the walls.

———

To treat dropsy, give vinegar and bitters in one-teaspoon doses, at night—keeping in mind that the father beset by horrors will favor camphor (two scruples should do) and that squills may inspire needless bleeding. Convulsions call for plasters at the throat—and, on occasion, amputation of the child's hands.

Heartsickness, or Saint John's complaint (to use the correct term), is akin to black fever, at least in respect of the lesions—but the site of these, if not the pattern, also suggests plague. Were apoplexy to accompany screws or bloody flux, however, or a wound of a particular size (three fingers across, say)—worms would then explain the rattling in the lungs.

The pages are marked in curious ways, though ornamental borders of this sort, especially those that exhibit insects, are far more common before 1700. Plague seems to favor green birds, as it happens, or rows of wagons and houses. Certain names are replaced with urns. Another anatomy presents the ribcage in the form of snakes—with winter scenes at the bottom of every column. Plans of the spine, furthermore, often include sickles, in addition to the cleavers near the numbers.

In folklore, the towns kill children for skulls. These are set atop sticks or crooks, the sockets filled with cloth. Relics are brought to a meadow, a pasture, a knoll—where the families tell pitiful tales at the funeral pile.

The skeletons in old schoolrooms—these are black, given the inscriptions. They list the illnesses, in order, and relate the terms of the murders. Fits, for instance, with bules—and then the king's evil. A man and a woman stabbed through the hands on a staircase.

A treatise concerning Mrs. Trundle's disease, from 1760, cites the demeanor of the bedsheets, and offers an inventory of hospital objects, beginning with a bistoury and a capital saw. The former, according to the annotation, is engraved with the surgeon's name. The latter has a stag handle, split in the middle. In certain editions, scarecrows stand in an anteroom—an error, I presume, despite mention of a dwarf-wall. The illustration, overleaf, exhibits four dogs on a cross.

II.

In the first postscript, the hearts are mistaken for dead birds. Doubtless the ants are thought a disappointment. When the horse becomes a house, furthermore, termites appear on the floor.

The room would be easier to see in an exploded view.

The sternum, imagined as a sword or a dagger, makes a more worrisome claim. The tail of the pancreas terminates at the spleen.

Listen for rales in the lungs and a catch in the throat.

When the child is supine, as here, the liver hides behind the ribs. The windpipe attracts spiders at night.

In the second postscript, a boy watches the body. It is said to resemble a table of beetles. The heart is said to resemble a skinned animal or a burnt skull. It waits in the rain, at any rate, like other objects.

Embalmed, it is properly brown. It will sink if you drop it into a pond.

In the third postscript, the wife is buried, or set afire, or brought by cart to the mourners. A later translation cites John, at great length, and places the bones and clothing in the road—beside the cleft, as the afternoon passes.

———

Maps of the body, in early anatomy, display the organs as houses in a town. The colors are quite bright—or rather dim. The heart is thought to contain eight rooms—or ruins, given the eventual corruption of the term.

In line drawings of a particular kind, the heavens divide the victims into wretched sections. The legend, decorated with garlands and the like, abbreviates each name. Diagrams of skeletons behave more obligingly, or at least provide a finer distraction.

Models of the heart, in wooden versions, in old hospitals—these can be nailed to walls or used for kindling. Blankets cover the skulls—while the wardrobe drops four stories.

Were you to arrange my organs on a table, the lungs, I expect, would sit below the hornets, and the heart at one o'clock.

Wound dolls, in the form of Devils, are marked at the throat, the hoof, the tail. The heads are stuffed with horsehair and stitched with wool. The letters concern amputation, but can also show the placement of veins.

Ax mannikins, for surgeons, are said to resemble nuns. Thorns can replace the eyes, surely, though seams are customary. Pinholes suggest a gloomier room, later in the year. The lips are black specks—grime or tar or soot.

Skeletons, on maps of the towns—such figures often replace annotations. In Bonelawn, as Bethlehem was once known, torches mean retreat or flight. In Mildred, there are rowboats for drownings. In Townsend, shovels and pickaxes for disease. Maps of the battlefields use red circles for smallpox and red dashes for blood. Bodies are shown as dots at the bottom of the sheet.

My recipe for tripe requires a slip of buff paper, a woman's name embossed at the top. A fold, lengthwise, should hide nine words. The hand should slant.

Calf's liver, potted, is better in winter. Calf's heart is simpler, despite the veins and clots. Sheep's lights, beaten and trimmed, and then plunged into boiling water, drained, dredged with flour, and baked for two hours—these are garnished with parsley.

Score in squares or present handsome gashes.

Silver should be placed one inch from the edge of the table—the knives, turned in, sitting below the glass, which will topple, or perhaps crack in your hand.

The plate should be white and without ornament. Address the left side first, except when crooknecks or parsnips are in evidence. Remember that the meat can sometimes bleed too amply.

The napkin will fall by the end of the meal.

To remove objects correctly, begin with your wife's position. If this is empty, begin with the child's. If the child's position is empty, carry the carving knife to the sideboard.

Gather the scraps in butcher paper or a tall jar.

III.

Disposition of the remains, in an upper room, as nighttime arrives—this accounts for the houndstooth pattern. A flannel housecoat (pointed yoke, open neck) and a gentleman's possessions (we have few, alas) do seem pleasant facts, certainly, save for the question of the insects. Bluebottles are more likely than houseflies, especially about the mouth, while beetles (carrion, for instance, and bark) are often seen beneath the sleeves.

Removal from the room, in the morning, assuming two bronze clocks, a lampshade, and a rope—but let us neglect the plan of the staircase, please.

The dissection tables display bell chains, dowels, twine. The rat-tail hinges are a bit too stout. Names are written out on the near side—brown letters for orphans, blue for Jews.

The clouts rust well, or stand at a charming slant.

The implements, brass and otherwise, are missing from some depictions.

In Germantown, a wooden arm falls afoul of the rail. In Red Bank, organs are replaced with artifacts —and, on occasion, rocks. In Pike Fork, widows are painted gray.

Measurement of the dead, like measurement of a bride, occurs as per local practice, and may require a catlin knife.

The horses and dogs are destroyed behind the morgue.

To examine the left atrium, posterior aspect, cut along the septum, ignoring the middle cardiac vein (awfully narrow and black, in this case) and the pulmonary trunk (or the remnant thereof)—and then hold the heart aloft. To examine the right atrium, cut out the lateral wall, disclosing the eustachian valve—though this is often absent in the adult heart. The arteries are best observed from above, except in the event of certain defects, such as those known to afflict widowers in cities. A cross section will show four holes (rather resembling a face, I am afraid) and two appendages, dark at the far end.

To examine the ventricles, in a frontal section, use fingers or shears. Discard in parts.

The embalming tables are adorned with gilt figures. Some later examples are famous for their claw-and-ball feet. What a pity, however, about the torn ribbon.

A porcelain basin sits beside a porcelain chamberpot. The cabinets favor eyebolts, strap hinges, white paint.

The jars of arsenic account for the cats.

If drams replace barn-gallons, and nails replace hands—doubtless this will ruin the view of the wounds. The first, at the throat, suits the room. The second, at the jaw, is perhaps too extravagantly red.

Superstition dictates that the head face west, and that the frame and grates form a cross. The slats are covered with matting—burlap, presumably, or stammel.

The mold grows best at night.

To prepare the remains, use equal parts turpentine (or ammonia, in summer) and mutton tallow (or rottenstone, if need be)—though scalding water will also suffice. Soak the brush in a tin pail. Males require straight-razors with dull blades and pearl handles—except, of course, in cases of decollation. To shut the eyes, use birdlime and wax. Suture the mouth with a length of wire.

The incision at the neck, just above the collarbone, on the right side—this should measure one inch across, keeping in mind the condition of the flesh and the size of the child. Locate the carotid artery. Introduce the solution, which should include, in addition to the usual elements, wormwood and gray sour—the latter in the absence of dye. Drain the blood through a cast-iron pipe.

———

Engravings after 1800 favor the more familiar sign, or something akin to it, though this is easily mistaken for a dead mouse or a bloody hand. A split-head teaspoon of about 1810, then, common in coffins, may startle one. A carving knife of roughly the same moment, such as the specimen found at the New Street house, will likely display letters and numbers—or, to be exact, a name and a date.

In various woodcuts, the heart appears as a crutch-cross or a pitchfork. The former, given this configuration of spikes, also means lightning—and fire, when events warrant. A Devil's staff, pointing east—perhaps this will remind you of Philip. Inverted, it means murder.

Portraits of the corpses indicate a different predicament, naturally, given the character of the town. In a parlor, red words on a dress. At a cannon, a bit of spittle on a lapel. In a wagon, which collapses, rats atop a claw-hammer coat.

Tradition calls for charcoal or black ink. The letter Y, imprinted on the skin, may suggest a thorn of some sort. The letter H is three blades. There is usually a name, too, I understand—the wife's, in blue dye.

Engravings on certain rings, in 1860—these reverse the initials, among other errors. The platinum items are a consolation, it turns out, though the ardent phrases appear in the wrong places. A copper trinket of about 1880, found with the garments, resembles a hatpin or a knitting needle, and omits the heart altogether.

TEN

My wife arranged the knives in a tidy row. Sometimes a game is made of such formations—don't you find? And so she collects the needles and he extracts the hairpins as—observe—the blanket turns black. Or so goes our conjecture, as quaint as the names of the places. Or the ax in the pattern of the house. It catches the light or dispatches a shadow—though this is more often the case for widowers, I think.

In certain histories of the romantic tale, ritual dictates a trembling of the hands.

Dowagers swallowed rings, silver and otherwise, on such occasions—though I have this point on poor authority. They would trace the initials and burn the pages. Sometimes they hung them on hooks. Yes—oh, well, no. Hers sat—once, that I recall—on the windowsill. The panes and the blinds, a woman in a gown. A geometry of nuptial detail. Which does put it grandly.

My wife kept the knife box. Caskets are also used for jewels—is this not pleasant to remember? Spinsters hung theirs on nails—though spikes were more common, I take it. The wall is white, the table blue, the door as clean as a hatchet. To claim an old phrase. Set yours in the drawer, please, or beneath the bedsheet. Wear the ashes, in the manner of a widow. Say the name.

In certain histories of ritual, romantic tales are nailed to caskets in the square.

The wife burns the husband's clothing. The husband stands at the end of the corridor, on every floor. We do embrace our examples, sometimes, with undue devotion. The town—it had been founded by a benedict. Commencing with burnt posts on a lawn. Our house was quite plain, I am afraid. Pause here, at the door. Present yourself at the window, as she had, and now remove yourself from view.